Nursery Rhyme Treasury

This book belongs to:

Ella

with lots of love & kisses
from Aunty Anne Dorothy
& Jonathan
x x x x

Nursery Rhyme Treasury

Illustrated by Leonie Shearing

Produced for Chad Valley Toys
242–246 Marylebone Road,
London, NW1 6JL

www.woolworths.co.uk

ISBN 978-1-4075-0514-5
Printed in China

Contents

Nursery Rhyme Characters

Action Rhymes

Animal Rhymes

Nonsense Rhymes

Counting Rhymes

Rhymes About Food

Bedtime Rhymes

Nursery Rhyme Characters

Jack and Jill

Jack and Jill went up the hill,
To fetch a pail of water;
Jack fell down and broke his crown,
And Jill came tumbling after.

Then up Jack got, and home did trot,
As fast as he could caper;
He went to bed, to mend his head,
With vinegar and brown paper.

Georgie Porgie

Georgie Porgie, pudding and pie,
Kissed the girls and made them cry;
When the boys came out to play,
Georgie Porgie ran away.

Mary, Mary, Quite Contrary

Mary, Mary, quite contrary,
How does your garden grow?
With silver bells and cockle shells
And pretty maids all in a row.

Tinker, Tailor

Tinker, tailor,
Soldier, sailor,
Rich man, poor man,
Beggarman, thief!

Humpty Dumpty

Humpty Dumpty sat on a wall,
Humpty Dumpty had a great fall;
All the king's horses and all the king's men
Couldn't put Humpty together again.

The Queen of Hearts

The Queen of Hearts,
She made some tarts
All on a summer's day.

The Knave of Hearts,
He stole the tarts
And took them clean away.

The King of Hearts,
Called for the tarts
And beat the knave full sore.

The Knave of Hearts,
Brought back the tarts
And vowed he'd steal no more.

Rain, Rain, Go Away

Rain, rain, go away,
Come again another day.
Little Jenny wants to play.

It's Raining, It's Pouring

It's raining, it's pouring,
The old man is snoring;
He went to bed and bumped his head
And couldn't get up in the morning!

Little Jack Horner

Little Jack Horner
Sat in the corner,
Eating his Christmas pie;
He stuck in his thumb,
And pulled out a plum,
And said, "What a good boy am I!"

Mary Had a Little Lamb

Mary had a little lamb
Its fleece was white as snow;
And everywhere that Mary went
The lamb was sure to go.

It followed her to school one day,
Which was against the rules;
It made the children laugh and play
To see a lamb at school.

The Grand Old Duke of York

Oh, the grand old Duke of York,
He had ten thousand men,
He marched them up to the top of the hill,
And he marched them down again.

And when they were up they were up,
And when they were down they were down,
And when they were only half way up,
They were neither up nor down.

Michael Finnegan

There was an old man called Michael Finnegan,
He grew whiskers on his chinnegan.
The wind came out and blew them in again,
Poor old Michael Finnegan.

Doctor Foster

Doctor Foster went to Gloucester
In a shower of rain;
He stepped in a puddle,
Right up to his middle,
And never went there again.

Robin and Richard

Robin and Richard were two pretty men;
They laid in bed till the clock struck ten;
Then up starts Robin and looks at the sky,
"Oh! Brother Richard, the sun's very high!
You go before, with the bottle and bag,
And I will come after on little Jack Hag."

Polly, Put the Kettle On

Polly, put the kettle on,
Polly, put the kettle on,
Polly, put the kettle on,
We'll all have tea.

Sukey, take it off again,
Sukey, take it off again,
Sukey, take it off again,
They've all gone away.

Old Mother Hubbard

Old Mother Hubbard
Went to the cupboard,
To fetch her poor dog a bone;
But when she got there
The cupboard was bare,
And so the poor dog had none.

Jackanory

I'll tell you a story
  Of Jackanory,
    And now my story's begun;
      I'll tell you another
        Of Jack his brother,
          And now my story's done.

There Was an Old Woman Who Lived In a Shoe

There was an old woman who lived in a shoe,
She had so many children she didn't know what to do;
She gave them some broth without any bread;
and scolded them soundly and sent them to bed.

Jack Sprat

Jack Sprat could eat no fat,
His wife could eat no lean,
And so between the two of them
They licked the platter clean.

Little Bo-Peep

Little Bo-Peep has lost her sheep,
And doesn't know where to find them;
Leave them alone, and they'll come home,
Bringing their tails behind them.

There Was a Little Girl

There was a little girl, and she had a little curl
Right in the middle of her forehead.
When she was good she was very, very good,
But when she was bad she was horrid.

Bobby Shaftoe

Bobby Shaftoe's gone to sea,
Silver buckles on his knee,
He'll come back and marry me,
Bonny Bobby Shaftoe.

Yankee Doodle

Yankee Doodle went to town,
Riding on a pony;
He stuck a feather in his hat,
And called it macaroni.

Yankee Doodle fa, so, la
Yankee Doodle dandy,
Yankee Doodle fa, so, la
Buttermilk and brandy.

Yankee Doodle went to town,
To buy a pair of trousers;
He swore he could not see the town,
For so many houses.

Lucy Locket

Lucy Locket lost her pocket,
Kitty Fisher found it,
Not a penny was there in it
Only ribbon round it.

Little Boy Blue

Little Boy Blue, come blow your horn,
The sheep's in the meadow, the cow's in the corn.
Where is the boy that looks after the sheep?
He's under a haycock, fast asleep.
Will you wake him? No, not I!
For if I do, he's sure to cry.

Old King Cole

Old King Cole
Was a merry old soul,
And a merry old soul was he;
He called for his pipe,
And he called for his bowl,
And he called for his fiddlers three.
Every fiddler had a fine fiddle,
And a very fine fiddle had he;
Oh there's none so rare
As can compare
With King Cole
   and his fiddlers three.

Little Miss Muffet

Little Miss Muffet
Sat on a tuffet,
Eating her curds and whey;
Along came a spider,
Who sat down beside her
And frightened Miss Muffet away.

Tom, Tom, the Piper's Son

Tom, Tom, the piper's son,
Stole a pig and away did run.
The pig was eat, and Tom was beat,
And Tom went roaring down the street.

There Was an Old Woman Tossed Up in a Blanket

There was an old woman tossed up in a blanket,
Seventeen times as high as the moon;
What she did there I could not but tell it,
For in her hand, she carried a broom.

"Old woman, old woman, old woman," said I,
"Where are you going to up so high?"
"To sweep the cobwebs from the sky.
And I shall be back again by and by."

Little Sally Waters

Little Sally Waters,
Sitting in the sun,
Crying and weeping,
For a young man.
Rise, Sally, rise,
Dry your weeping eyes,
Fly to the east,
Fly to the west,
Fly to the one you love the best.

Hector Protector

Hector Protector was dressed all in green;

Hector Protector was sent to the Queen.

The Queen did not like him,

No more did the King;

So Hector Protector was sent back again.

Jack Be Nimble

Jack be nimble,
Jack be quick,
Jack jump over
The candlestick.

Ride A Cock-Horse

Ride a cock-horse to Banbury Cross
To see a fine lady upon a white horse.
Rings on her fingers and bells on her toes,
She shall have music wherever she goes.

Simple Simon

Simple Simon met a pieman
Going to the fair;
Said Simple Simon to the pieman,
"Let me taste your ware."

Tommy Tucker

Little Tommy Tucker
Sings for his supper:
What shall we give him?
Brown bread and butter.
How shall he cut it
Without a knife?
How can he marry
Without a wife?

Oh Dear, What Can the Matter Be?

Oh dear, what can the matter be?
Dear, dear, what can the matter be?
Oh dear, what can the matter be?
Johnny's so long at the fair.

He promised he'd buy me a basket of posies,
A garland of lilies, a garland of roses,
A little straw hat to set off the blue ribbons
That tie up my bonny brown hair.

Oh dear, what can the matter be?
Dear, dear, what can the matter be?
Oh dear, what can the matter be?
Johnny's so long at the fair.

Monday's Child Is Fair of Face

Monday's child is fair of face,
Tuesday's child is full of grace,
Wednesday's child is full of woe,
Thursday's child has far to go,
Friday's child is loving and giving,
Saturday's child works hard for a living,
And the child that is born on the Sabbath day
Is bonny and blithe, and good and gay.

Action Rhymes

Here We Go Round the Mulberry Bush

Here we go round the mulberry bush,
The mulberry bush, the mulberry bush,
Here we go round the mulberry bush,
On a cold and frosty morning.

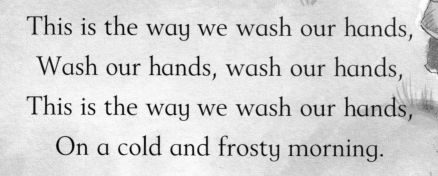

This is the way we wash our hands,
Wash our hands, wash our hands,
This is the way we wash our hands,
On a cold and frosty morning.

This is the way we brush our hair,
Brush our hair, brush our hair,
This is the way we brush our hair,
On a cold and frosty morning.

This is the way we go to school,
Go to school, go to school,
This is the way we go to school,
On a cold and frosty morning.

Here Is the Church

Here is the church,

Interlace fingers.

Here is the steeple,

Point index fingers to make the steeple.

Open the doors,

Open thumbs out to represent the doors.

And here are the people.

Turn hands over and wiggle fingers to show the people.

Here is the parson, going upstairs,

Walk fingers of one hand up the fingers of the other hand.

And here he is a-saying his prayers.

Place palms together.

Row, Row, Row Your Boat

Mime a rowing action throughout as the rhyme suggests.

Row, row, row your boat
Gently down the stream.
Merrily, merrily, merrily, merrily,
Life is but a dream.

This Little Piggy

Pretend each of the child's toes is a little piggy.

Begin with the biggest toe and finish by tickling under the child's foot!

This little
piggy went to
market,

This little piggy
stayed at home,

This little piggy
had roast beef,

This little piggy
had none,

And this little piggy
cried, "Wee, wee, wee"
All the way home.

A Face Game

Here sits the Lord Mayor;   *Forehead*

Here sits his two men;   *Eyes*

Here sits the cock;   *Right cheek*

Here sits the hen;   *Left cheek*

Here sit the little chickens;   *Tip of nose*

Here they run in;   *Mouth*

Chinchopper, chinchopper,

Chinchopper, chin!   *Chuck the chin*

68

Lavender's Blue

Lavender's blue, dilly, dilly,
Lavender's green;
When I am king, dilly, dilly,
You shall be queen.

If You're Happy and You Know It

If you're happy and you know it,
Clap your hands.
If you're happy and you know it,
Clap your hands.
If you're happy and you know it,
And you really want to show it,
If you're happy and you know it,
Clap your hands.

Incey Wincey Spider

Incey Wincey spider climbing up the spout,

Use all fingers to show the spider climbing up the spout.

Down came the rain and washed the spider out.

Wriggle your fingers to show the rain.

Out came the sun, and dried up all the rain,

Make a big circle with your arms.

Incey Wincey spider climbed up the spout again.

Repeat the action for the first line.

71

This Is the Way the Ladies Ride

This is the way the ladies ride:
Tri, tre, tre, tree,
Tri, tre, tre, tree!
This is the way the ladies ride:
Tri, tre, tre, tre, tri-tre-tre-tree!

This is the way the gentlemen ride:
Gallop-a-trot,
Gallop-a-trot!
This is the way the gentlemen ride:
Gallop-a-gallop-a-trot!

This is the way the farmers ride:
Hobbledy-hoy,
Hobbledy-hoy!
This is the way the farmers ride:
Hobbledy hobbledy-hoy!

Wash, Hands, Wash

Wash, hands, wash,
Daddy's gone to plough;
If you want your hands washed,
Have them washed now.

See-Saw, Margery Daw

See-saw, Margery Daw,
Jack shall have a new master;
He shall have but a penny a day,
Because he can't work any faster.

Round and Round the Garden

Round and round the garden
Like a teddy bear;

Draw a circle with your finger round

and round the child's palm.

One step, two step,

Walk fingers up the child's arm.

Tickle you under there!

Tickle the child under their arm!

Okey Cokey

You put your left arm in, your left arm out,
In, out, in, out, shake it all about,
You do the okey cokey, and you turn around,
And that's what it's all about.

Oh, the okey cokey,
Oh, the okey cokey,
Oh, the okey cokey,
Knees bend, arms stretch,
Ra ra ra!

Rub a Dub Dub

Rub a dub dub,
Three men in a tub,
And how do you think they got there?
The butcher, the baker,
The candlestick-maker,
They all jumped out of a rotten potato,
It was enough to make a man stare.

The Wheels on the Bus

The wheels on the bus go round and round,
Round and round, round and round,
The wheels on the bus go round and round,
All day long.

Move hands in a circular motion.

The wipers on the bus go swish, swish, swish,
Swish, swish, swish, swish, swish, swish,
The wipers on the bus go swish, swish, swish,
All day long.

Waggle both extended index fingers.

The horn on the bus goes beep! beep! beep!
Beep! beep! beep! beep! beep! beep!
The horn on the bus goes beep! beep! beep!
All day long.

Pretend to press a horn.

The people on the bus go chat, chat, chat,

Chat, chat, chat, chat, chat, chat,

The people on the bus go chat, chat, chat,

All day long.

Put thumb on rest of extended fingers. Hold your thumb and fingers out straight to make a beak shape and open and close it.

The children on the bus bump up and down,

Up and down, up and down,

The children on the bus bump up and down,

All day long.

'Bump' up and down on a chair.

To Market, To Market

To market, to market, to buy a fat pig,
Home again, home again, jiggety jig;
Ride to the market to buy a fat hog,
Home again, home again, jiggety jog.

To market, to market,
To buy a plum bun,
Home again, home again,
Market is done.

Ring-a-Ring o' Roses

Ring-a-ring o' roses,
A pocket full of posies.
A-tishoo! A-tishoo!
We all fall down!

Teddy Bear, Teddy Bear

Do the same as Teddy!

Teddy Bear, Teddy Bear,
Touch the ground.

Teddy Bear, Teddy Bear,
Turn around.

Teddy Bear, Teddy Bear,
Show your shoe.

Teddy Bear, Teddy Bear,
That will do.

Teddy Bear, Teddy Bear,
Run upstairs.

Teddy Bear, Teddy Bear,
Say your prayers.

Teddy Bear, Teddy Bear,
Turn out the light.

Teddy Bear, Teddy Bear,
Say goodnight.

I'm a Little Teapot

I'm a little teapot short and stout,
Here's my handle, here's my spout,
When I get my steam up hear me shout,
Tip me up and pour me out.

Animal Rhymes

Baa, Baa, Black Sheep

Baa, baa, black sheep,
Have you any wool?
Yes sir, yes sir,
Three bags full;

One for the master,
And one for the dame,
And one for the little boy
Who lives down the lane.

Hickory, Dickory, Dock,

Hickory, dickory, dock,
The mouse ran up the clock.
The clock struck one,
The mouse ran down,
Hickory, dickory, dock.

The Owl and the Pussy-Cat

The Owl and the Pussy-cat went to sea
In a beautiful pea-green boat,
They took some honey,
and plenty of money,
Wrapped up in a five-pound note.

The owl looked up to the stars above,
And sang to a small guitar,
"Oh lovely Pussy! Oh Pussy, my love,
What a beautiful pussy you are,
You are, you are!
What a beautiful pussy you are!"

Once I Saw a Little Bird

Once I saw a little bird
Come hop, hop, hop;
So I cried, "Little bird,
Will you stop, stop, stop?"
I was going to the window,
To say, "How do you do?"
But he shook his little tail,
And far away he flew.

Three Blind Mice

Three blind mice, three blind mice.
See how they run, see how they run!
They all ran after the farmer's wife,
Who cut off their tails with a carving knife,
Did you ever see such a thing in your life?
As three blind mice.

Oh Where, Oh Where?

Oh where, oh where has my little dog gone?
Oh where, oh where can he be?
With his ears cut short and his tail cut long,
Oh where, oh where is he?

Ding, Dong, Bell

Ding, dong, bell,

Pussy's in the well.

Who put her in?

Little Johnny Green.

Who pulled her out?

Little Tommy Trout.

What a naughty boy was that,

To try and drown poor pussy cat.

Who never did him any harm,

And killed the mice in his father's barn.

The Ostrich

Here is the ostrich
straight and tall
Nodding his head
above us all.

Here is the hedgehog
prickly and small,
Rolling himself
into a ball.

Here is the spider
scuttling around.
Treading so lightly
on the ground.

Here are the birds
that fly so high,
Spreading their wings
across the sky.

Here are the children
fast asleep,
And in the night
the owls do peep,
"Tuit tuwhoo, tuit
tuwhoo!"

Cock-a-Doodle-Doo!

Cock-a-doodle-doo!
My dame has lost her shoe;
My master's lost his fiddling stick,
And doesn't know what to do.

Cock-a-doodle-doo!
What is my dame to do?
Till master finds his fiddling stick,
She'll dance without her shoe.

Cock-a-doodle-doo!
My dame has found her shoe,
And master's found his fiddling stick,
Sing cock-a-doodle-doo.

Cock-a-doodle-doo!
My dame will dance with you,
While master fiddles his fiddling stick,
For dame and doodle doo.

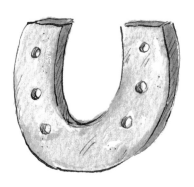

For Want of a Nail

For want of a nail, the shoe was lost;
For want of the shoe, the horse was lost;
For want of the horse, the rider was lost;
For want of the rider, the battle was lost;
For want of the battle, the kingdom was lost;
And all from the want of a horseshoe nail.

I Had a Little Cow

I had a little cow;
Hey-diddle, ho-diddle!
I had a little cow, and it had a little calf;
Hey-diddle, ho-diddle! and there's my song half.

Ladybird! Ladybird!

Ladybird! Ladybird! Fly away home,
Night is approaching, and sunset is come.
The herons are flown to their trees by the Hall;
Felt, but unseen, the damp dewdrops fall.
This is the close of a still summer day;
Ladybird! Ladybird! Haste! Fly away!

Birds of a Feather

Birds of a feather flock together
And so will pigs and swine;
Rats and mice shall have their choice,
And so shall I have mine.

The North Wind Doth Blow

The north wind doth blow,
And we shall have snow,
And what will poor Robin do then?
Poor thing!

He'll sit in a barn,
And keep himself warm,
And hide his head under his wing.
Poor thing!

Higglety, Pigglety, Pop!

Higglety, pigglety, pop!
The dog has eaten the mop;
The pig's in a hurry,
The cat's in a flurry,
Higglety, pigglety, pop!

Sing a Song of Sixpence,

Sing a song of sixpence
A pocket full of rye;
Four-and-twenty blackbirds
Baked in a pie.
When the pie was opened
The birds began to sing;
Wasn't that a dainty dish
To set before the king?

The king was in his counting-house
Counting out his money;
The queen was in the parlour
Eating bread and honey.
The maid was in the garden
Hanging out the clothes,
When down flew a blackbird
And pecked off her nose!

Hickety Pickety, My Black Hen

Hickety Pickety, my black hen,
She lays eggs for gentlemen,
Gentlemen come every day
To see what my black hen does lay.

The Lion and the Unicorn

The Lion and the Unicorn
Were fighting for the crown;
The Lion beat the Unicorn
All around the town.
Some gave them white bread,
And some gave them brown;
Some gave them plum cake,
And drummed them out of town.

Little Robin Redbreast

Little Robin Redbreast
Sat upon a rail:
Niddle-noddle went his head!
Wiggle-waggle went his tail.

Pussy Cat, Pussy Cat

Pussy cat, pussy cat, where have you been?

I've been to London to visit the Queen.

Pussy cat, pussy cat, what did you do there?

I frightened a little mouse under her chair.

I Had a Little Hen

I had a little hen, the prettiest ever seen,
She washed me the dishes, and kept the house clean:
She went to the mill to fetch me some flour,
She brought it home in less than an hour;
She baked me my bread, she brewed me my ale,
She sat by the fire and told many a fine tale.

Nonsense Rhymes

The Man In the Moon

The man in the moon
Came down too soon,
And asked his way to Norwich;
He went by the south,
And burnt his mouth
With supping cold pease porridge.

Peter Piper

Peter Piper picked a peck of pickled pepper;
A peck of pickled pepper Peter Piper picked;
If Peter Piper picked a peck of pickled pepper,
Where's the peck of pickled pepper Peter Piper picked?

Hey Diddle Diddle

Hey diddle diddle,
The cat and the fiddle,
The cow jumped over the moon;
The little dog laughed
To see such sport,
And the dish ran away
with the spoon.

Goosey, Goosey, Gander

Goosey, goosey, gander,
Whither shall I wander?
Upstairs and downstairs
And in my lady's chamber.
There I met an old man
Who would not say his prayers,
So I took him by the left leg,
And threw him down the stairs.

Sneeze on Monday

Sneeze on Monday, sneeze for danger;

Sneeze on Tuesday, kiss a stranger;

Sneeze on Wednesday, get a letter;

Sneeze on Thursday, something better;

Sneeze on Friday, sneeze for sorrow;

Sneeze on Saturday, see your sweetheart tomorrow.

There Was a Crooked Man

There was a crooked man,
and he went a crooked mile,
He found a crooked sixpence
against a crooked stile;
He bought a crooked cat,
which caught a crooked mouse,
And they all lived together
in a little crooked house.

Tweedledum and Tweedledee

Tweedledum and Tweedledee
Agreed to have a battle,
For Tweedledum said Tweedledee
Had spoiled his nice new rattle.
Just then flew down a monstrous crow,
As big as a tar-barrel,
Which frightened both the heroes so,
They quite forgot their quarrel.

Counting
Rhymes

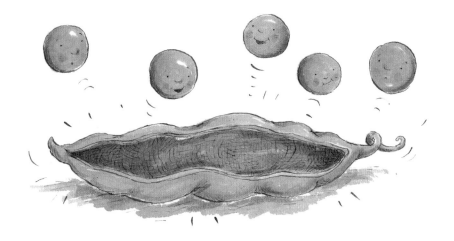

Five Little Ducks

Five little ducks went swimming one day,
Over the hills and far away,
Mother Duck said "Quack, quack, quack, quack",
But only four little ducks came back.

One little duck went swimming one day,
Over the hills and far away,
Mother Duck said "Quack, quack, quack, quack",
And five little ducks came swimming back.

Days in the Month

Thirty days hath September,
April, June, and November;
All the rest have thirty-one,
Excepting February alone,
And that has twenty-eight days clear
And twenty-nine in each leap year.

One, Two, Buckle My Shoe

One, two,
Buckle my shoe;

Three, four,
Knock at the door;

Five, six,
Pick up sticks;

Seven, eight,
Lay them straight;

Nine, ten,
A good fat hen;

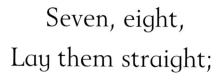

Eleven, twelve,
Dig and delve;

Thirteen, fourteen,
Maids a-courting;

Fifteen, sixteen,
Maids in the kitchen;

Seventeen, eighteen,
Maids a-waiting;

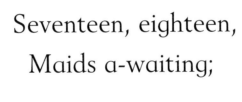

Nineteen, twenty,
My plate's empty.

Five Little Peas

Five little peas in a pea-pod pressed,
One grew, two grew, and so did all the rest.
They grew, and they grew, and they did not stop,
Until one day the pod went … POP!

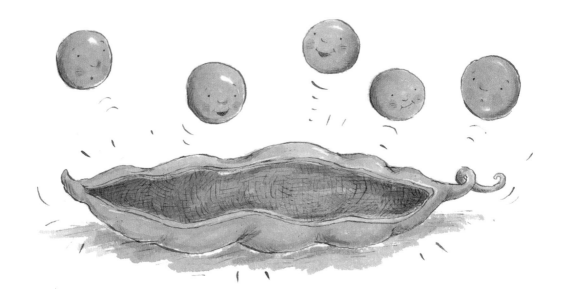

Magpies

One for sorrow, two for joy,
Three for a girl, four for a boy,
Five for silver, six for gold,
Seven for a secret never to be told.

Chook, Chook, Chook

Chook, chook, chook, chook, chook,
Good morning, Mrs Hen.
How many chickens have you got?
Madam, I've got ten.

Four of them are yellow,
And four of them are brown,
And two of them are speckled red,
The nicest in the town.

Two Little Dicky Birds

Two little dicky birds sitting on a wall,
One named Peter, one named Paul.
Fly away, Peter!
Fly away, Paul!
Come back, Peter!
Come back, Paul!

One, Two, Three, Four, Five

One, two, three, four, five,
Once I caught a fish alive.
Six, seven, eight, nine, ten,
Then I let it go again.

Why did you let it go?
Because it bit my finger so.
Which finger did it bite?
This little finger on the right.

Build a House with Five Bricks

Build a house with five bricks,
One, two, three, four, five.
Put a roof on top,
And a chimney too.
Where the wind blows through!

I Saw Three Ships

I saw three ships come sailing by,
Come sailing by, come sailing by;
I saw three ships come sailing by,
On New Year's Day in the morning.

And what do you think was in them then,
Was in them then, was in them then?
And what do you think was in them then,
On New Year's Day in the morning?

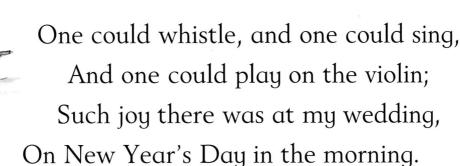

Three pretty girls were in them then,
Were in them then, were in them then;
Three pretty girls were in them then,
On New Year's Day in the morning.

One could whistle, and one could sing,
And one could play on the violin;
Such joy there was at my wedding,
On New Year's Day in the morning.

Five Little Monkeys

Five little monkeys
walked along the shore;
One went a-sailing,
Then there were four.

Four little monkeys
climbed up a tree;
One of them fell down,
Then there were three.

Three little monkeys
found a pot of glue;
One got stuck in it,
Then there were two.

Two little monkeys
found a raisin bun;
One ran away with it,
Then there was one.

One little monkey
cried all afternoon;
So they put him in an aeroplane
And sent him to the moon.

One Man Went to Mow

One man went to mow, went to mow a meadow,
One man and his dog Spot,
Went to mow a meadow.

Two men went to mow, went to mow a meadow,
Two men, one man and his dog, Spot,
Went to mow a meadow.

Three men went to mow, went to mow a meadow,
Three men, two men, one man and his dog, Spot,
Went to mow a meadow.

Four men went to mow, went to mow a meadow,
Four men, three men, two men, one man and his dog, Spot
Went to mow a meadow.

Five Fat Sausages

Five fat sausages frying in a pan,
All of a sudden one went "BANG!"

Four fat sausages frying in a pan,
All of a sudden one went "BANG!"

Three fat sausages frying in a pan,
All of a sudden one went "BANG!"

Two fat sausages frying in a pan,
All of a sudden one went "BANG!"

One fat sausage frying in a pan,
All of a sudden it went "BANG!"

And there were NO sausages left!

Rhymes About Food

Pease Pudding Hot

Pease pudding hot,
Pease pudding cold,
Pease pudding in the pot,
Nine days old.

Some like it hot,
Some like it cold,
Some like it in the pot,
Nine days old.

Pop Goes the Weasel

Up and down the City Road
In and out the Eagle,
That's the way the money goes.
Pop goes the weasel!

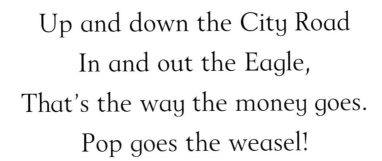

Half a pound of tuppenny rice,
Half a pound of treacle,
Mix it up and make it nice,
Pop goes the weasel!

Every night when I go out
The monkey's on the table;
Take a stick and knock it off,
Pop goes the weasel!

Oranges and Lemons

Oranges and lemons,
Say the bells of St Clements.
You owe me five farthings,
Say the bells of St Martins.
When will you pay me?
Say the bells of Old Bailey.
When I grow rich,
Say the bells of Shoreditch.

Hot Cross Buns

Hot cross buns!
Hot cross buns!
One a penny, two a penny,
Hot cross buns!

Hot cross buns!
Hot cross buns!
If you have no daughters
Give them to your sons.

Jelly on the Plate

Jelly on the plate
Jelly on the plate
Wibble, wobble,
Wibble, wobble,
Jelly on the plate.

Sweeties in the jar,
Sweeties in the jar,
Shake them up,
Shake them up,
Sweeties in the jar.

Candles on the cake,
Candles on the cake,
Blow them out,
Blow them out,
Puff, PUFF, PUFF!

Pat-a-Cake

Pat-a-cake, pat-a-cake, baker's man,
Bake me a cake as fast as you can.
Roll it, and prick it, and mark it with a "B"
And put it in the oven for Baby and me!

Bedtime Rhymes

Bedtime

The evening is coming, the sun sinks to rest;
The rooks are all flying straight home to the nest.
"Caw!" says the rook, as he flies overhead;
"It's time little people were going to bed!"

The flowers are closing; the daisy's asleep;
The primrose is buried in slumber so deep.
Shut up for the night is the pimpernel red;
It's time little people were going to bed!

The butterfly, drowsy, has folded its wing;
The bees are returning, no more the birds sing.
Their labour is over, their nestlings are fed;
It's time little people were going to bed!

Go to Bed First

Go to bed first,
A golden purse;

Go to bed second,
A golden pheasant;

Go to bed third,
A golden bird.

I See the Moon

I see the moon,
And the moon sees me;
God bless the moon,
And God bless me.

Boys and Girls, Come Out to Play

Boys and girls, come out to play,
The moon doth shine as bright as day!
Leave your supper and leave your sleep,
And meet your playfellows in the street.

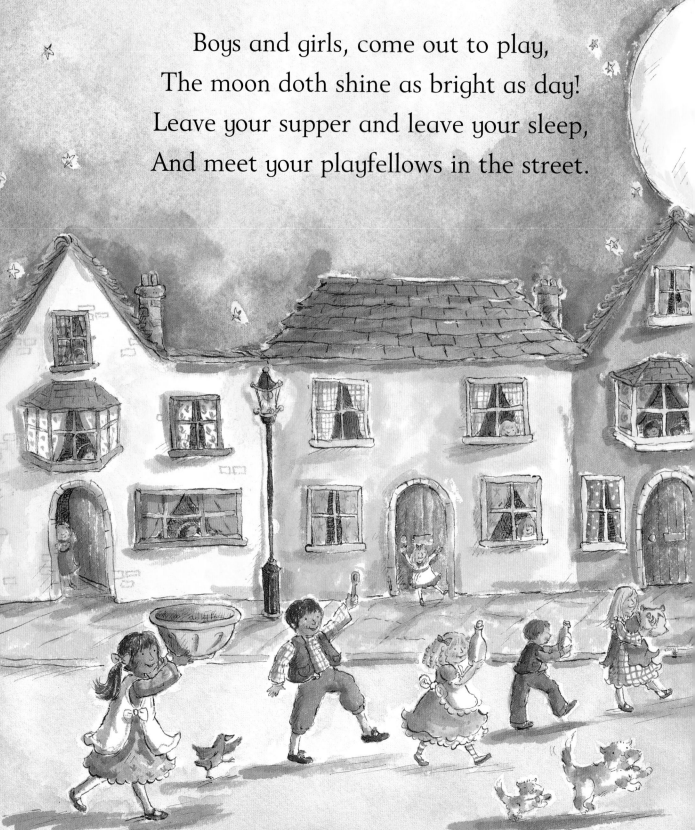

Come with a whistle and come with a call,
Come with a good will or not at all.
Up the ladder and down the wall,
A halfpenny loaf will serve us all.
You find milk, and I'll find flour,
And we'll have a pudding in half an hour.

Sleep Little Child

Sleep little child, go to sleep,
Mother is here by your bed.
Sleep little child, go to sleep,
Rest on the pillow your head.

The world is silent and still,
The moon shines bright on the hill,
Then creeps past the window sill.

Sleep little child,
go to sleep,
Oh sleep,
go to sleep.

Star Light, Star Bright

Star light, star bright,
First star I see tonight,
I wish I may, I wish I might,
Have the wish I wish tonight.

Go to Bed Late

Go to bed late,
Stay very small;
Go to bed early,
Grow very tall.

Twinkle, Twinkle, Little Star

Twinkle, twinkle, little star,
How I wonder what you are!
Up above the world so high,
Like a diamond in the sky.

When the blazing sun is gone,
When he nothing shines upon,
Then you show your little light,
Twinkle, twinkle, all the night.

Then the traveller in the dark,
Thanks you for your tiny spark,
He could not see which way to go,
If you did not twinkle so.

In the dark blue sky you keep,
And often through my curtains peep,
For you never shut your eye,
'Til the sun is in the sky.

As your bright and tiny spark,
Lights the traveller in the dark –
Though I know not what you are,
Twinkle, twinkle, little star.

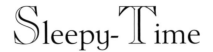

Sleepy-Time

Sleepy-time has come for my baby,
Baby now is going to sleep.
Kiss Mama good night
And we'll turn out the light,
While I tuck you in bed
'Neath your covers tight.
Sleepy-time has come for my baby,
Baby now is going to sleep.

Tumbling

In jumping and tumbling
We spend the whole day,
'Til night by arriving
Has finished our play.

What then? One and all,
There's no more to be said,
As we tumbled all day,
So we tumble to bed.

Golden Slumbers

Golden slumbers kiss your eyes,
Smiles await you when you rise;
Sleep, pretty baby, do not cry,
And I will sing a lullaby.

Bye, Baby Bunting

Bye, baby bunting,
Daddy's gone a-hunting,
Gone to get a rabbit-skin,
To wrap my baby bunting in.

Bed in Summer

In winter I get up at night,
And dress by yellow candle-light.
In summer, quite the other way,
I have to go to bed by day.

I have to go to bed and see
The birds still hopping on the tree,
Or hear the grown-up people's feet
Still going past me in the street.

And does it not seem hard to you,
When all the sky is clear and blue,
And I should like so much to play,
To have to go to bed by day?

Come to Bed, says Sleepy-Head

"Come to bed," says Sleepy-head,
"Tarry a while," says Slow;
"Put on the pot," says Greedy-gut,
"Let's sup before we go."

Go to Bed, Tom

Go to bed, Tom,
Go to bed, Tom,
Tired or not, Tom,
Go to Bed, Tom.

Bedtime

Down with the lambs
Up with the lark,
Run to bed children
Before it gets dark.

Wee Willie Winkie

Wee Willie Winkie
Runs through the town,
Upstairs and downstairs
In his nightgown.
Rapping at the window,
Crying through the lock,
Are the children all in bed?
For now it's eight o'clock.

Hush, Little Baby

Hush, little baby, don't say a word,
Papa's gonna buy you a mocking bird.

If that mocking bird don't sing,
Papa's gonna buy you a diamond ring.

If that diamond ring turns to brass,
Papa's gonna buy you a looking-glass.

If that looking-glass gets broke,
Papa's gonna buy you a billy goat.

If that billy goat don't pull,
Papa's gonna buy you a cart and mule.

If that cart and mule turn over,
Papa's gonna buy you a dog named Rover.

If that dog named Rover won't bark,
Papa's gonna buy you a horse and cart.

If that horse and cart fall down,
You'll still be the sweetest little baby in town.

Diddle, Diddle, Dumpling

Diddle, diddle, dumpling, my son John
Went to bed with his trousers on;
One shoe off, and the other shoe on,
Diddle, diddle, dumpling, my son John.

How Many Miles to Babylon?

How many miles to Babylon?
Three score and ten.
Can I get there by candle-light?
Yes, and back again.
If your heels are nimble and light,
You may get there by candle-light.

Hush-a-Bye, Baby

Hush-a-bye, baby, on the tree top,
When the wind blows the cradle will rock;
When the bough breaks the cradle will fall,
Down will come baby, cradle and all.

See a Pin

See a pin and pick it up,
All the day you'll have good luck;
See a pin and let it lay,
Bad luck you'll have all the day!

Sleep, Baby, Sleep

Sleep, baby, sleep,
Your father keeps the sheep;
Your mother shakes the dreamland tree
And from it fall sweet dreams for thee;
Sleep, baby, sleep.

Sleep, baby, sleep,
The large stars are the sheep;
The little stars are the lambs, I guess,
And the gentle moon is the shepherdess;
Sleep, baby, sleep.

Sleep, baby, sleep,
Your father keeps the sheep;
Your mother guards the lambs this night,
And keeps them safe till morning light;
Sleep, baby, sleep.

Brahms' Lullaby

Lullaby, and good night,
With rosy bed light,
With lilies overspread,
Is my baby's sweet bed.

Lay you down now, and rest,
May your slumber be blessed!
Lay you down now, and rest,
May your slumber be blessed!

Lullaby, and good night,
You're your mother's delight,
Shining angels beside
My darling abide.

Soft and warm is your bed,
Close your eyes and rest your head.
Soft and warm is your bed,
Close your eyes and rest your head.

Up the Wooden Hill

Up the wooden hill
To Bedfordshire.
Down Sheet Lane
To Blanket Fair.

The Mouse's Lullaby

Oh, rock-a-bye, baby mouse, rock-a-bye, so!
When baby's asleep to the baker's I'll go,
And while he's not looking I'll pop out of a hole,
And bring to my baby a fresh penny roll.

Little Fred

When little Fred went to bed,
He always said his prayers;
He kissed Mama, and then Papa,
And straightaway went upstairs.

Now the Day is Over

Now the day is over,
Night is drawing nigh,
Shadows of the evening
Steal across the sky.

Now the darkness gathers,
Stars begin to peep,
Birds and beasts and flowers
Soon will be asleep.

The Man in the Moon

The man in the moon looked out of the moon,
Looked out of the moon and said,
"'Tis time for all children on the earth
To think about getting to bed!"

Index of First Lines

Acknowledgements

Brahms' Lullaby, Johannes Brahms; Now the Day is Over, Sabine Baring-Gould; The Mouse's Lullaby, Palmer Cox; Golden Slumbers, Thomas Dekker; Twinkle Twinkle, Little Star, Jane Taylor; Bed in Summer, Robert Louis Stevenson.

Every effort has been made to trace the ownership of all material. In the event of any question arising as to the use of the material, the publisher will be happy to make the necessary correction in future printings.